Nancy Hall

Spell*well*

Book

D

Educators Publishing Service, Inc.
Cambridge and Toronto

Cover design by Hugh Price

Illustrations by Alan Price and Hugh Price

Educators Publishing Service, Inc.
31 Smith Place, Cambridge, MA 02138-1089

Printed in the U.S.A.   ISBN 0-8388-2197-9

February 2000 Printing

CONTENTS

Copy the words your teacher gives you under Classroom Words. Fold this page back along the dotted line so that only the Pretest column shows. Write the words your teacher dictates.

Spell*well* Words	**Corrections**	**Pretest**
1. bananas	_____	1. _____
2. closet	_____	2. _____
3. credit	_____	3. _____
4. divide	_____	4. _____
5. dozen	_____	5. _____
6. drama	_____	6. _____
7. federal	_____	7. _____
8. habitat	_____	8. _____
9. melody	_____	9. _____
10. modern	_____	10. _____
11. novel	_____	11. _____
12. president	_____	12. _____
13. prisoner	_____	13. _____
14. products	_____	14. _____
15. recommend	_____	15. _____
16. several	_____	16. _____
17. talented	_____	17. _____
18. travel	_____	18. _____
19. volume	_____	19. _____

Outlaw Word

20. chocolate	_____	20. _____

Classroom Words

21. _____	_____	21. _____
22. _____	_____	22. _____
23. _____	_____	23. _____
24. _____	_____	24. _____
25. _____	_____	25. _____

Compare your words with the spelling list. Write the words you did not know in the Corrections column. If all, or all but one, of the words are correct, use the following for your spelling words: **balanced, recommendation, division, dramatize, misery, monitor, productive,** and **catalog.** Write them in the Corrections column along with the Classroom Words; then do the Alternative Homework this week.

Can you solve these equations to find a spelling word? When subtracting, cross out the letters; when adding, put the letters at the *end* of the word.

For example: worthless - th + d - less =
worthless + d - less =
worlessd - less =
worlessd = word

1. secretary - tary + d - se + it = _____

2. individual - ual + e - in = _____

3. improve - im + duc - ve + ts = _____

4. spring - s + son - ng + er = _____

5. postal - po + en - s + ted = _____

6. abandon - a + an - don + as = _____

7. impression - sion + i - im + dent = _____

8. revolt - re + u - t + me = _____

9. inches + oco - in + late - es = _____

10. defendant - de + er - ant + al - n = _____

11. enclosure - ure + et - en = _____

12. director - tor + om - di + mend = _____

13. contradict - con + vel - dict = _____

14. mineral - in + o - ra + dy = _____

15. smoldering - l + n - s - ing = _____

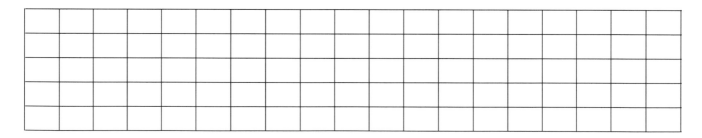

Write your Classroom Words in alphabetical order with one letter in each square.

Which five Spell*well* Words were not used on this page? _____

_____

_____

Alternative Homework: In your reading book, find 12 words that you want to learn. Write these words in the Corrections column on page 1. Make a personal dictionary by folding thirteen sheets of paper in half and stapling them on the fold. Write one letter of the alphabet on the upper outside corner of each page. Then write each of your spelling words under its first letter, and write a definition for it.

Write spelling words from this week's list that can substitute for the underlined words in each sentence.

1. We buy eggs <u>twelve at a time</u>. by the ☐☐☐☐☐

2. Our class wrote and performed this <u>exciting and suspenseful story</u>. ☐☐☐☐☐☐

3. One must be <u>gifted</u> to play the piano so beautifully. ☐☐☐☐☐☐☐

4. Can you <u>praise and suggest</u> a good Indian restaurant? ☐☐☐☐☐☐☐☐☐

5. Every four years we elect the <u>leader</u> of our country. ☐☐☐☐☐☐☐☐☐

6. The award-winning author has written a new <u>book of fiction</u>. ☐☐☐☐☐

7. Many people now <u>go from one place to another</u> by airplane. ☐☐☐☐☐☐

8. <u>Quite a few</u> friends of mine speak Spanish well. ☐☐☐☐☐☐

9. You can find an article on ants in the first <u>book</u> of the encyclopedia. ☐☐☐☐☐☐☐

10. The <u>person held in jail</u> tried to escape last night. ☐☐☐☐☐☐☐

11. Please pick up your clothes and hang them in the <u>clothes storage</u>. ☐☐☐☐☐☐

12. Cream and cheese are two <u>things made</u> from milk. ☐☐☐☐☐☐☐

13. I keep singing that lovely <u>tune</u> over and over. ☐☐☐☐☐

14. Monkeys like to eat <u>narrow yellow fruits</u>, and so do I. ☐☐☐☐☐☐

15. Get a pizza and <u>cut it into equal parts</u> with your sister. ☐☐☐☐☐

16. Streams and lakes are the <u>natural living area</u> for freshwater fish. ☐☐☐☐☐☐☐

17. The old building was remodeled and looks very <u>contemporary</u>. ☐☐☐☐☐☐

18. Declaring war is a <u>national</u> power. ☐☐☐☐☐☐

19. The brave firefighters get all the <u>praise</u> for saving our home. ☐☐☐☐☐☐

Write your Outlaw and Classroom Words.
Circle in color any little words in them.

Alternative Homework: On a separate sheet of paper, write twelve of your spelling words, one on each line. Next to each word, write a word related to it in some way; it may be a plural of the word or have the same root.

Sort the phrases below into the categories of living and nonliving things.

chocolate pudding

monkey eating bananas

a credit card

honey, a product of bees

president of Student Council

several snowmen

a mothproof closet

a dozen caterpillars

a modern composer

a popular novel

a handcuffed prisoner

the radio's volume

a talented artist

a television drama

the melody of "Beauty and the Beast"

a skunk and its habitat

federal taxes

a travel agent

a class divided into groups

Living Things

1. _____
2. _____
3. _____
4. _____
5. _____
6. _____
7. _____
8. _____
9. _____
10. _____

Nonliving Things

1. _____
2. _____
3. _____
4. _____
5. _____
6. _____
7. _____
8. _____
9. _____
10. _____

Fill in the last blank with an appropriate phrase of your own.

Which Spell*well* Word was not used on this page? _____

Write your Classroom Words in color below.

_____

_____

_____

Alternative Homework: Sort your spelling words into living and nonliving things by writing them in the columns above.

Find the spelling words hidden in the circle. The words overlap each other so that the last letter of one word becomes the first letter of the next word. Three other words have been added: *leap*, *lap*, and *alp*. Make up a story using these nine spelling words, and write it below. It may be mysterious, scary, or funny. Be sure to spell well.

[Word circle]
Top arc (clockwise): commendramalpresidentalent
Bottom arc: novleaproductseveralaprison
(with connecting letters: rec... at left and ...edoo...e at right)

_____

_____

_____

_____

_____

_____

_____

_____

_____

_____

_____

_____

_____

_____

_____

_____

_____

_____

_____

_____

Alternative Homework: Try to create a round-robin circle using eight of your spelling words. Trade circles with another student working on Alternative Homework. After you find the words, use them to write a story on the lines above, using the directions given.

Copy the words your teacher gives you under Classroom Words. Fold this page back along the dotted line so that only the Pretest column shows. Write the words your teacher dictates.

Pretest	**Corrections**	**Spell*well* Words**
1. _____	_____	1. cucumber
2. _____	_____	2. demand
3. _____	_____	3. deposit
4. _____	_____	4. diameter
5. _____	_____	5. duplex
6. _____	_____	6. equal
7. _____	_____	7. frequent
8. _____	_____	8. medium
9. _____	_____	9. microwave
10. _____	_____	10. pretend
11. _____	_____	11. propeller
12. _____	_____	12. quiet
13. _____	_____	13. reflect
14. _____	_____	14. rodent
15. _____	_____	15. slogan
16. _____	_____	16. total
17. _____	_____	17. triangle
18. _____	_____	18. United States

Outlaw Words

19. _____	_____	19. iron
20. _____	_____	20. piano

Classroom Words

21. _____	_____	21. _____
22. _____	_____	22. _____
23. _____	_____	23. _____
24. _____	_____	24. _____
25. _____	_____	25. _____

Compare your words with the spelling list. Write the words you did not know in the Corrections column. If all, or all but one, of the words are correct, use the following for your spelling words: **democracy, media, patriotism, prohibit, republic, stadium, totally,** and **variety.** Write them in the Corrections column along with the Classroom Words; then do the Alternative Homework this week.

Fifteen spelling words have been divided into syllables and then separated into two columns. Make the words whole again by drawing a line from the first syllable in column one to the remaining syllable or syllables in column two. Notice that each first syllable is an open syllable with a long vowel at the end. Write the whole word on the line next to the last syllable.

1. ro	am • e • ter	_____
2. tri	cum • ber	_____
3. di	et	_____
4. cu	di • um	_____
5. slo	dent	_____
6. me	an • gle	_____
7. e	tal	_____
8. to	cro • wave	_____
9. qui	tend	_____
10. du	flect	_____
11. re	pos • it	_____
12. fre	qual	_____
13. de	gan	_____
14. mi	quent	_____
15. pre	plex	_____

Write your Classroom Words, sorting them into three categories: nouns (persons, places, things), verbs (actions a person can do), and all other words.

Nouns

_____

_____

_____

_____

Verbs

_____

_____

_____

_____

All Other Words

_____

_____

_____

_____

Which spelling words were not used on this page?

_____   _____

_____   _____

_____

Alternative Homework: In your reading book, find 12 words (some with long vowels) that you want to learn. Write them in the Corrections column on page 6. Then write all of your spelling words and their definitions in your personal dictionary.

Find the word in each line that is improperly used or spelled and cross it out. Then choose a spelling word that better fits the sentence; write it on the line.

1. Terry was so quite working in the library that we didn't see her. _____

2. Because we are such freequent bus riders, we get a discount. _____

3. The Untied Stats consists of fifty individual states. _____

4. We will reflex the sun's rays off the mirror to produce heat. _____

5. The porpeller moves the water with a force that drives the boat. _____

6. Irony is a metal used in the manufacture of steel. _____

7. Two families live in the duplus. _____

8. Let's put some tomatoes and a cumbersome in the salad. _____

9. A roadent is a gnawing mammal with big teeth. _____

10. When a paino is played poorly, it can give you a headache. _____

11. If you add 343 plus 4478, the totem is 4821. _____

12. A micron oven cooks food in a very short time. _____

13. The distance across a circle is called the diater. _____

14. Let's portend that it isn't raining. _____

15. To be fair, let's divide the pie into three unequal pieces. _____

16. A customer can defend money back on a defective radio. _____

17. Be sure to depot your money in the bank before it closes. _____

Write the Classroom Words below on the steps, using a colored pencil for the vowels.

Alternative Homework: Scramble the letters of each of your first eight spelling words. Then trade papers with another classmate with Alternative Homework this week; try to unscramble each other's words.

How are the following words related?
In each case, think about how the first two words are connected.
Then apply the same relationship to find the missing spelling word.

Sometimes the first two words are *synonyms*.

1. **myth** is to **legend** as **motto** is to _____

2. **part** is to **section** as **sum** is to _____

3. **big** is to **large** as **average** is to _____

4. **seldom** is to **rare** as **often** is to _____

5. **request** is to **ask** as **insist** is to _____

6. **launder** is to **wash** as **press** is to _____

7. **uncover** is to **reveal** as **imagine** is to _____

Sometimes the first two words are *antonyms* or opposites:

8. **small** is to **huge** as _____ is to **noisy**

9. **appear** is to **disappear** as _____ is to **unequal**

10. **save** is to **spend** as _____ is to **withdraw**

Sometimes the words describe *one part of a whole* and *the whole*:

11. **France** is to **Europe** as _____ is to **North America**

12. **diagonal** is to **square** as _____ is to **circle**

13. **wheel** is to **bike** as _____ is to **helicopter**

14. **strings** are to **violin** as **keys** are to _____

15. **bed** is to **bunk bed** as **apartment** is to _____

Sometimes the words are *a category* and *an example from it*:

16. **reptile** is to **rattlesnake** as _____ is to **rat**

17. **tool** is to **hammer** as **oven** is to _____

18. **fruit** is to **orange** as **vegetable** is to _____

19. **number** is to **three** as **shape** is to _____

Sometimes the first word is *an object* and the second tells *what it does*.

20. **magnifying glass** is to **enlarge** as **mirror** is to _____

How many Classroom Words do you recall?
Write them in the margins.

Alternative Homework: Find out when and why the Statue of Liberty was built. Then write a report telling what you have learned. If you have visited the monument, tell what was most interesting to you. If you haven't visited it, tell what you would like to see if you ever go there.

Can you dress up these simple sentences by adding details that give the information requested on each line?

1. **We have equal rights.**

   (Who has them?) _____ have _____ rights.

   (Tell why.) _____ have _____ rights because

   _____ .

2. **The moon reflects.**

   (What ?) The moon _____ _____ .

   (Tell how and when.) The moon _____

   from the _____ _____ .

3. **This state is part of the United States.**

   (Which state?) The state of _____ is part of _____ _____ .

   (Add a word to describe the state.) The _____ state of _____

   is part of the _____ _____ .

   I like this state because _____

   _____ .

4. **A triangle has straight sides.**

   (Tell how many.) A _____ has _____ straight sides.

5. **The slogan is clever.**

   (Which slogan?) The _____ is clever.

   (Tell why.) The _____ is clever because

   _____ .

6. **Shoes are medium-sized.**

   (Tell whose shoes.) _____ shoes are _____-sized.

   (Add what kind of shoes.) _____ _____ shoes are

   _____-sized.

7. **We pretend.**

   (Tell what.) We _____ _____ .

   (Now tell when.) We _____ _____ .

8. **I have a pet rodent.**

   (Tell what kind of rodent.) I have a pet _____ which is a _____ .

   (Tell where it came from.) I have a pet _____ named _____ which

   I got _____ .

Write your Classroom Words, adding *s* or another ending if you can. _____

   _____

   _____

Alternative Homework: Select eight of your spelling words and write each in a simple sentence. Then try to add details that answer questions like those above.

Copy the words your teacher gives you under Classroom Words. Fold this page back along the dotted line so that only the Pretest column shows. Write the words your teacher dictates.

Spellwell Words	Corrections	Pretest
1. arrest		1.
2. assorted		2.
3. borrow		3.
4. cartoon		4.
5. charming		5.
6. export		6.
7. forbid		7.
8. gorilla		8.
9. harvest		9.
10. history		10.
11. inventory		11.
12. marble		12.
13. normal		13.
14. orbit		14.
15. ordinary		15.
16. quarrel		16.
17. quarter		17.
18. sparkle		18.
19. support		19.

Outlaw Words

20. guard		20.
21. guitar		21.

Classroom Words

22.		22.
23.		23.
24.		24.
25.		25.

Compare your words with the spelling list. Write the words you did not know in the Corrections column. If all, or all but one, of the words are correct, use the following for your spelling words: **forfeit, glossary, laboratory, monarch, orchid, ordinarily, torrent,** and **wheelbarrow**. Write them in the Corrections column along with the Classroom Words; then do the Alternative Homework this week.

Look at the words below. Find spelling words that contain these small words, and write them beneath the appropriate word. Next, think of other words that come from these words, and add them to each list. You may add prefixes and suffixes, changing any spelling as necessary. Use a dictionary if you wish.

vent

_____

_____

_____

sort

_____

_____

_____

rest

_____

_____

_____

harm

_____

_____

_____

spar

_____

_____

_____

port

_____

_____

_____

cart

_____

_____

story

_____

_____

vest

_____

_____

About Face!

What does *qu* do to the sound of *ar*?
It makes *ar* sound like _____ .

Write two Spell*well* Words with *qu*.

_____   _____

Which Spell*well* Words were *not* used?

_____

_____

_____

_____

Write your Classroom Words; then circle any little words in them.

_____

_____

Alternative Homework: In your reading book, find 13 words with *ar* and *or* that you want to learn. Write them in the Corrections column on page 11. Then write all of your spelling words and their definitions in your personal dictionary.

Find the spelling word that fits the meaning; then write it in syllables in the boxes.

1. This is often funny. = ☐☐☐ ☐☐☐☐

2. A night watchman is one. = ☐☐☐☐

3. Diamonds do this. = ☐☐☐☐ ☐☐☐

4. Police do this to speeders. = ☐☐ ☐☐☐☐

5. Folk singers often play this. = ☐☐☐ ☐☐☐

6. This equals twenty-five cents. = ☐☐☐☐ ☐☐☐

7. It is large, strong, and hairy. = ☐☐ ☐☐☐ ☐☐

8. You may do this with a brother or sister sometimes. = ☐☐☐☐ ☐☐☐

9. Satellites do this around a planet. = ☐☐ ☐☐☐

10. This is the name for gathering the crops in the fall. = ☐☐☐ ☐☐☐☐

11. Parents do this when they say no. = ☐☐☐☐ ☐☐☐

12. Some statues are made of this. = ☐☐☐☐ ☐☐

13. This means to send goods to another country to be sold. = ☐☐☐ ☐☐☐☐

14. This is what your temperature usually is. = ☐☐☐☐ ☐☐☐

15. Without this, a tent will not stand. = ☐☐☐ ☐☐☐☐

16. This describes a group of mixed or varied items. = ☐☐ ☐☐☐☐☐ ☐☐☐☐

17. You do this when you need something you don't have. = ☐☐☐☐ ☐☐☐☐

18. This describes a person or thing that is delightful. = ☐☐☐☐☐ ☐☐☐

19. You study this in school. = ☐☐☐☐ ☐☐ ☐☐

20. This means counting the store stock once a year. = ☐☐ ☐☐☐ ☐☐ ☐☐

Which Spell*well* Word was not used on this page? _____

Write your Classroom Words in color on the lines below.

_____

_____

_____

_____

Alternative Homework: Choose your longest spelling word and make as many words as possible out of the letters.

Decipher the following message, using the letters that correspond to the numbers below. Write the letters over the numbers as shown. Circle the spelling words you find in the message, and write them on the lines below.

A	B	C	D	E	F	G	H	I	J	K	L	M	N	O	P	Q	R	S	T	U	V	W	X	Y	Z
1	2	3	4	5	6	7	8	9	10	11	12	13	14	15	16	17	18	19	20	21	22	23	24	25	26

S O S
19 15 19 !   8 1 22 5   2 5 5 14   9 14   19 16 1 3 5   19 9 24 20 25

4 1 25 19 .   14 15 18 13 1 12   12 1 21 14 3 8   23 9 20 8   15 14 12 25

17 21 1 18 20 5 18   15 6   6 21 5 12   21 19 5 4 .   2 21 20   14 15 23

19 20 21 3 11   9 14   15 18 2 9 20 .   20 15 15 11

9 14 22 5 14 20 15 18 25   15 6   16 15 19 19 9 2 12 5

3 1 21 19 5 19 .   6 9 14 4   1 19 19 15 18 20 5 4

16 18 15 2 12 5 13 19 .   20 8 9 19   15 18 4 9 14 1 18 25

6 12 9 7 8 20   13 1 25   2 5   8 9 19 20 15 18 25   21 14 12 5 19 19

23 5   7 5 20   19 21 16 16 15 18 20 .   19 5 14 4

8 5 12 16   19 15 15 14 !

_____

_____

_____

_____

Write your Outlaw and Classroom Words in alphabetical order._____

_____

_____

_____

_____

Alternative Homework: Do the activity above.

Using some of the phrases below, write ten good sentences.

guard these marbles   eyes that sparkle

export bananas   arrested the criminal

borrow a book   quarrel over shoes

forbid us to go   play a guitar

a charming village   the harvest moon

the mother gorilla   drew a cartoon

Alternative Homework: Read about the monarch butterfly. Describe how this butterfly looks, and tell any interesting facts you learn about it. Why do you think it is called "monarch"? Use some spelling words in your essay.

Copy the words your teacher gives you under Classroom Words. Fold this page back along the dotted line so that only the Pretest column shows. Write the words your teacher dictates.

Pretest	**Corrections**	**Spell*well* Words**
1. _____	_____	1. behavior
2. _____	_____	2. calendar
3. _____	_____	3. equator
4. _____	_____	4. familiar
5. _____	_____	5. flavor
6. _____	_____	6. governor
7. _____	_____	7. grammar
8. _____	_____	8. humor
9. _____	_____	9. inspector
10. _____	_____	10. lunar
11. _____	_____	11. muscular
12. _____	_____	12. particular
13. _____	_____	13. polar
14. _____	_____	14. popular
15. _____	_____	15. similar
16. _____	_____	16. vapor
17. _____	_____	17. visitor

Outlaw Words

18. _____	_____	18. favorite
19. _____	_____	19. sword
20. _____	_____	20. toward

Classroom Words

21. _____	_____	21. _____
22. _____	_____	22. _____
23. _____	_____	23. _____
24. _____	_____	24. _____
25. _____	_____	25. _____

Compare your words with the spelling list. Write the words you did not know in the Corrections column. If all, or all but one, of the words are correct, use the following for your spelling words: **aviator, dictator, temporary, mayor, particularly, similarity, singular,** and **humorous.** Write them in the Corrections column along with the Classroom Words; then do the Alternative Homework this week.

Sort the Spell*well* Words according to the patterns below.

Words Ending in *or*

_____
_____
_____
_____
_____
_____
_____
_____

Words Ending in *ar*

_____
_____
_____
_____
_____
_____
_____
_____
_____
_____

Can you think of another word for each pattern?

_____   _____

Which spelling word has a silent *w*? _____

Which Outlaw Words were not used on this page? _____

Write your Classroom Words beginning with the shortest and ending with the longest.

_____

_____

_____

_____

_____

Alternative Homework: In your reading book, find 12 words (some with *-ar* and *-or*) that you want to learn. Write them in the Corrections column on page 16. Then write all of your spelling words and their definitions in your personal dictionary.

Write spelling words from this week's list that can substitute for the underlined words in each sentence.

1. The word *ain't* is considered to be bad <u>English usage</u>.

2. We plan future events by looking at the <u>chart showing the days</u>.

3. Halfway between the North and South Poles is the <u>imaginary line</u>.

4. Sometimes in school we are graded on our <u>way of acting</u>.

5. The spaceship made a successful <u>moon-related</u> landing.

6. Our state must elect a new <u>head of government</u>.

7. The <u>person who examines things</u> is looking over our building.

8. The Olympic skier had very <u>strong, well-developed</u> legs.

9. When water boils, <u>steam</u> rises into the air.

10. No one laughed at the <u>funniness</u> of our jokes.

11. These two sports are <u>very much alike</u>.

12. We must clean up because a <u>guest</u> is coming.

13. What <u>particular taste</u> of ice cream do you like?

14. Long ago, a knight used a <u>large, heavy blade</u> to defend himself.

15. The announcer's voice was <u>known from before</u>.

16. Admiral Byrd was the first person to fly over <u>arctic</u> regions.

Write five questions using your Classroom Words.

_____

_____

_____

_____

_____

Which four spelling words were not used on this page?_____

_____

Alternative Homework: Write questions using nine of your spelling words. Then trade papers with another Alternative speller and answer each other's questions.

Mark the following statements *T* for true or *F* for false. Then underline the spelling word and write it in the box.

_____ 1. Wild behavior is often annoying to others.

_____ 2. No one has ever made a successful lunar landing.

_____ 3. The equator is two hundred miles north of here.

_____ 4. Tennis and football are very similar.

_____ 5. The governor is always a man.

_____ 6. Polar bears love to eat broccoli.

_____ 7. A sword has a two-sided blade.

_____ 8. A sense of humor is a good thing to have.

_____ 9. Pistachio ice cream is the favorite of most people.

_____ 10. Most calendars show 14 months.

_____ 11. "Don't never" is considered bad grammar.

_____ 12. You must be muscular to lift heavy weights.

Write the spelling words that begin with the sixth letter of the alphabet.

_____

Write the spelling words that begin with the fifth letter from the end of the alphabet.

_____

Write four true or false statements using the four Spell*well* and Outlaw Words not used on this page.

_____

_____

_____

_____

Write the Classroom Words anywhere on this page and color the vowels.

Alternative Homework: Write ten true or false statements using your spelling words. Trade papers with another Alternative speller and answer each other's statements with *T* or *F* .

Write a newspaper story using one of the headlines below. Circle the headline you will use. Try to include all the necessary facts. Tell *who* the story is about, *what* happened, *where* it took place, along with *when*, *how*, and *why*. Use some spelling words in your story.

LUNAR LANDING A SUCCESS
POLAR EXPEDITION DEPARTS AGAIN
CLASS MAKES TRIP TO EQUATOR
CALENDAR ADDS 30 DAYS TO SCHOOL YEAR
FIRE INSPECTOR CLOSES SCHOOL
GOVERNOR CREATES NEW HOLIDAY IN MARCH
POPULAR TV STAR IS SCHOOL VISITOR
PIZZA VOTED FAVORITE SCHOOL LUNCH

_____
_____
_____
_____
_____
_____
_____
_____
_____
_____
_____
_____
_____
_____
_____
_____
_____
_____
_____
_____
_____
_____

Alternative Homework: Make a headline using one of your spelling words. Then, following the directions above, write a news story on the lines provided.

Copy the words your teacher gives you under Classroom Words. Fold this page back along the dotted line so that only the Pretest column shows. Write the words your teacher dictates.

Spell*well* Words	**Corrections**	**Pretest**
1. advertise	_____	1. _____
2. curly	_____	2. _____
3. desert	_____	3. _____
4. disturb	_____	4. _____
5. during	_____	5. _____
6. figures	_____	6. _____
7. furnish	_____	7. _____
8. hamburger	_____	8. _____
9. jury	_____	9. _____
10. murder	_____	10. _____
11. natural	_____	11. _____
12. occur	_____	12. _____
13. pattern	_____	13. _____
14. plural	_____	14. _____
15. squirrel	_____	15. _____
16. surprised	_____	16. _____
17. thirsty	_____	17. _____
18. verdict	_____	18. _____

Outlaw Words

19. berry	_____	19. _____
20. bury	_____	20. _____
21. mirror	_____	21. _____

Classroom Words

22. _____	_____	22. _____
23. _____	_____	23. _____
24. _____	_____	24. _____
25. _____	_____	25. _____

Compare your words with the spelling list. Write the words you did not know in the Corrections column. If all, or all but one, of the words are correct, use the following for your spelling words: **absurd, burdensome, burial, curfew, machinery, murmured, raspberry,** and **sheriff.** Write them in the Corrections column along with the Classroom Words; then do the Alternative Homework this week.

Write a friend's first name that has at least six letters. _____
Now write each Spell*well* Word below. Count the number of letters in common with the letters in this name, and give yourself 1 point for each letter in common. If there are *no* letters in common, give yourself 20 points. If there are more than five letters the same, give yourself 10 points.

For example, if you wrote "Shirley," *hamburger* has three letters in common: *h, r, e.* Although *hamburger* has two *r*'s, you may only count one, since Shirley only has one *r*.

Spell*well* Words	Points		Spell*well* Words	Points
1. _____	_____		10. _____	_____
2. _____	_____		11. _____	_____
3. _____	_____		12. _____	_____
4. _____	_____		13. _____	_____
5. _____	_____		14. _____	_____
6. _____	_____		15. _____	_____
7. _____	_____		16. _____	_____
8. _____	_____		17. _____	_____
9. _____	_____		18. _____	_____

My Total Score: _____

Which spelling for the sound /er/ is used most often in the middle of a word? _____

Which two spelling words rhyme with *airy*? _____

Which Outlaw Word was not used on this page? _____

Write your Classroom Words on the lines below and circle each letter *e* in red.

_____

_____

_____

_____

Alternative Homework: In your reading book, find 13 words with *er, ir,* or *ur* that you would like to learn. Write these words in the Corrections column on page 21. Then write the words and their definitions in your personal dictionary.

Look at each group below. Which spelling word will complete the puzzle? The horizontal word (across) is a synonym for, or means the same as, the spelling word. The vertical word (up and down) is its antonym or opposite. Write the spelling word in the squares.

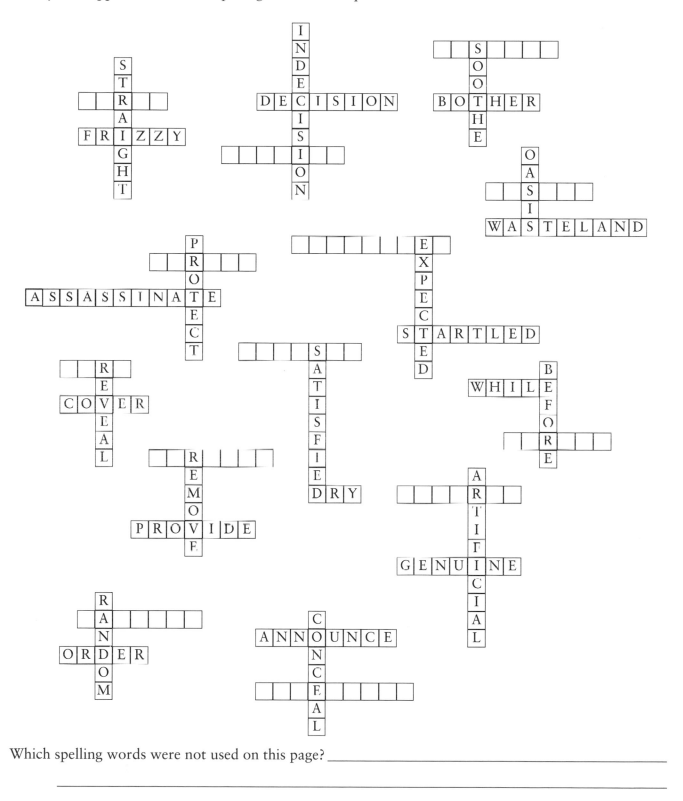

Which spelling words were not used on this page? _____

_____

_____

Alternative Homework: Write any twelve of your spelling words. Write an antonym next to each word that has one. Beside the remaining words, write an equal sign (=) and a synonym.

The words in **boldface** are spelled in reverse order. Write the letters in correct order above those in boldface. Then read the story and answer the questions.

You may be **desirprus** to learn there is a rodent, related to the **lerriuqs,** that looks like a tiny kangaroo. Its name is **aobrej**. With its eight-inch tail, it is about fifteen inches overall; it has whiskers, button eyes, short front legs, and long, **lufrewop** hind legs. It is **larutan** for the jerboa to walk on its back legs, using its tail for balance. When **debrutsid** or frightened, it gets away quickly in bounding leaps, just like a kangaroo. The jerboa's large head, big eyes, and silky, yellowish-brown fur give it a comical look. These animals live in the **stresed** of Asia, Africa, and the southwestern United States. **Gnirud** the day, they stay deep underground in burrows. At night, they come to the surface to gather food, mostly nuts and **seirreb**, which they stuff into fur-lined pouches on the outside of their cheeks. They can carry a lot of food back to their nest in these pouches. Jerboas never get **ytsriht**. Their food combines with the oxygen they breathe to produce water. Have you ever heard of an animal so well-suited to its **tatibah**?

Do you remember the facts?

What does a jerboa look like? _____

_____

How does it use its tail? _____

Describe the habitat of the jerboa._____

_____

What does a jerboa eat? _____

How does it carry food? _____

Why doesn't this animal ever get thirsty?_____

_____

Give synonyms for the following words:

1. frizzy   _____

2. happen   _____

3. announce _____

4. numbers   _____

5. a guide   _____

6. a panel   _____

Write the Outlaw and Classroom Words in the margins; underline the vowels.

Alternative Homework: Write a story about an animal you have owned or would like to own. Tell what the animal looks like, what its behavior is, and what your responsibilities as pet owner are.

Find the spelling words hidden in the circle. The words overlap each other so that the last letter or letters of one word become the first letter or letters of the next word. The following words have been added: *red, yes, live, yam, room, rip,* and *loaf.* Make up a story using the ten spelling words. It may be mysterious, scary, or funny. Be sure to spell well.

buryesquireliverdicthirstyamurderoom
(circular word puzzle)

_____

Write your Classroom Words in capital letters in the margins.

Alternative Homework: Try to create a round-robin circle using eight of your spelling words. Trade circles with another student working on Alternative Homework. After you find the words, use them to write a story on the lines above, following the directions given.

Copy the words your teacher gives you under Classroom Words. Fold this page back along the dotted line so that only the Pretest column shows. Write the words your teacher dictates.

Pretest	**Corrections**	**Spell*well* Words**
1. _____	_____	1. attachment
2. _____	_____	2. brotherhood
3. _____	_____	3. childhood
4. _____	_____	4. dampness
5. _____	_____	5. delightful
6. _____	_____	6. department
7. _____	_____	7. environment
8. _____	_____	8. equipment
9. _____	_____	9. excitement
10. _____	_____	10. fellowship
11. _____	_____	11. membership
12. _____	_____	12. narrowness
13. _____	_____	13. painful
14. _____	_____	14. penmanship
15. _____	_____	15. settlement
16. _____	_____	16. sickness
17. _____	_____	17. wilderness
18. _____	_____	18. wonderful

Outlaw Words

| 19. _____ | _____ | 19. errand |
| 20. _____ | _____ | 20. error |

Classroom Words

21. _____	_____	21. _____
22. _____	_____	22. _____
23. _____	_____	23. _____
24. _____	_____	24. _____
25. _____	_____	25. _____

Compare your words with the spelling list. Write the words you did not know in the Corrections column. If all, or all but one, of the words are correct, use the following for your spelling words: **falsehood, judgment, likelihood, merriment, numbness, scholarship, soreness,** and **sportsmanship**. Write them in the Corrections column along with the Classroom Words; then do the Alternative Homework this week.

Look at the words below. Find spelling words that contain these small words, and write them beneath the appropriate word. Next, think of other words that come from these words, and add them to each list. You may add prefixes and suffixes, changing the spelling as necessary. Use a dictionary if you wish.

set

_____

_____

_____

low

_____

_____

_____

part

_____

_____

_____

light

_____

_____

_____

wild

_____

_____

_____

cite

_____

_____

_____

man

_____

_____

_____

Iron

_____

_____

_____

ember

_____

_____

_____

Write two spelling words that begin with *er*. _____ _____

What sound does *er* make in these words? _____

Which Spell*well* Words were not used on this page? _____

_____

_____

_____

Write your Classroom Words in alphabetical order below.

1. _____   2. _____

3. _____   4. _____

5. _____

Alternative Homework: In your reading book, find 12 words that you want to learn. Write them in the Corrections column on page 26. Then write all of your spelling words and their definitions in your personal dictionary.

Write spelling words from this week's list that can substitute for the underlined words in each sentence.

1. During my years of growing up, I lived in Atlanta.

2. Most basements have a great deal of moisture.

3. The Division of the Treasury prints United States money.

4. Do you have legible handwriting?

5. Roanoke Island was the first small village in America.

6. This is where I made the mistake in subtraction.

7. The snow-covered pines look marvelous in the moonlight.

8. It is important to protect our natural surroundings.

9. The people who belong to this club will meet next week.

10. You need a lot of gear for deep-sea fishing.

11. As a tot, I had a deep feeling of connection to my teddy bear.

12. My aunt asked me to do another task outside the house for her.

13. My friends and I enjoy hiking in uninhabited, wooded areas.

14. The small width of the canal allows one boat to pass at a time.

15. We felt the thrill of the parade as we got nearer.

16. We had a very pleasing time on our field trip.

17. My broken arm is aching and makes me cry.

18. Chicken pox is a common childhood illness.

Write two Spell*well* Words not used above that are synonyms.

_____

_____

Write your Classroom Words; then circle in color any little words in them.

_____

_____

_____

_____

_____

Alternative Homework: Choose your longest spelling word and make as many words as you can out of the letters.

Decipher the following message, using the letters that correspond to the numbers below. Write the letters over the numbers as shown. Circle the spelling words you find in the message, and write them on the lines below.

A	B	C	D	E	F	G	H	I	J	K	L	M	N	O	P	Q	R	S	T	U	V	W	X	Y	Z
1	2	3	4	5	6	7	8	9	10	11	12	13	14	15	16	17	18	19	20	21	22	23	24	25	26

H E L P

8 5 12 16 !   20 8 5   13 5 13 2 5 18 19 8 9 16   15 6   15 21 18
(HELP! THE MEMBERSHIP OF OUR)

8 9 11 9 14 7   3 12 21 2   16 12 1 14 14 5 4   1
(HIKING CLUB PLANNED A)

23 15 14 4 5 18 6 21 12   20 18 9 16   20 15   1   23 15 15 4 5 4
(WONDERFUL TRIP TO A WOODED)

5 14 22 9 18 15 14 13 5 14 20 .   2 21 20   19 15 13 5   15 6   21 19
(ENVIRONMENT. BUT SOME OF US)

13 1 4 5   1 14   5 18 18 15 18 :   23 5   6 15 18 7 15 20   20 15
(MADE AN ERROR: WE FORGOT TO)

16 1 3 11   15 21 18   5 17 21 9 16 13 5 14 20 .   14 15 23   23 5
(PACK OUR EQUIPMENT. NOW WE)

1 18 5   3 1 13 16 9 14 7   9 14   20 8 5
(ARE CAMPING IN THE)

23 9 12 4 5 18 14 5 19 19   23 9 20 8   2 21 7 19 ,   2 5 1 18 19 ,
(WILDERNESS WITH BUGS, BEARS,)

4 1 13 16 14 5 19 19 ,   1 14 4   16 1 9 11 6 21 12   6 5 5 20 .
(DAMPNESS, AND PAINFUL FEET.)

16 12 5 1 19 5   18 5 19 3 21 5   21 19 !
(PLEASE RESCUE US!)

_____
_____
_____
_____

Write your Outlaw and Classroom Words, beginning with the longest.

_____
_____
_____
_____

Alternative Homework: Do the activity above.

Look at the suffixes below and think of words that rhyme. For example, under *ship* one might write *whip* or *sip*. Remember that rhyming words are not always spelled the same. Write at least three rhyming words. Next, write all of your spelling words under the correct suffix. Then, looking at the words you have listed, write a poem with at least eight rhyming lines. After you read your poem aloud, give it a title.

ful

_____
_____
_____
_____
_____
_____
_____

hood

_____
_____
_____
_____
_____
_____
_____

ness

_____
_____
_____
_____
_____
_____
_____

ment

_____
_____
_____
_____
_____
_____
_____

ship

_____
_____
_____
_____
_____
_____
_____

_____

_____
_____
_____
_____
_____
_____
_____
_____

Alternative Homework: Make rhymes with your Alternative spelling words; then write a poem on the lines above, using some of those rhyming words.

Copy the words your teacher gives you under Classroom Words. Fold this page back along the dotted line so that only the Pretest column shows. Write the words your teacher dictates.

Spell*well* Words	**Corrections**	**Pretest**
1. celebrate	_____	1. _____
2. century	_____	2. _____
3. citizen	_____	3. _____
4. concert	_____	4. _____
5. excellent	_____	5. _____
6. except	_____	6. _____
7. introduce	_____	7. _____
8. justice	_____	8. _____
9. necessary	_____	9. _____
10. office	_____	10. _____
11. precise	_____	11. _____
12. produce	_____	12. _____
13. recently	_____	13. _____
14. recite	_____	14. _____
15. recycle	_____	15. _____
16. silence	_____	16. _____
17. sincere	_____	17. _____
18. success	_____	18. _____

Outlaw Words

19. certain	_____	19. _____
20. curtain	_____	20. _____

Classroom Words

21. _____	_____	21. _____
22. _____	_____	22. _____
23. _____	_____	23. _____
24. _____	_____	24. _____
25. _____	_____	25. _____

Compare your words with the spelling list. Write the words you did not know in the Corrections column. If all, or all but one, of the words are correct, use the following for your spelling words: **ancestor, ceremony, certificate, license, necessity, official, pesticide,** and **rhinoceros.** Write them in the Corrections column along with the Classroom Words; then do the Alternative Homework this week.

Write your first name (no nicknames). _____
Now write each Spell*well* Word below. Count the number of letters in common with the letters in your name, and give yourself 1 point for each letter in common. If there are *no* letters in common, give yourself 20 points. If there are more than five letters the same, give yourself 10 points.

If you wrote "Frank," it has 0 letters in common with *except*, but two letters in common with *celebrate: r, a.*

Spell*well* Words	Points	Spell*well* Words	Points
1. _____	_____	10. _____	_____
2. _____	_____	11. _____	_____
3. _____	_____	12. _____	_____
4. _____	_____	13. _____	_____
5. _____	_____	14. _____	_____
6. _____	_____	15. _____	_____
7. _____	_____	16. _____	_____
8. _____	_____	17. _____	_____
9. _____	_____	18. _____	_____

My Total Score: _____

Underline all the *ce* combinations in your spelling words on page 31.

How many are there? _____ What letter does *ce* sound like? _____

Circle all the *ci* combinations in your spelling words. How many are there? _____

Ci usually has the sound of _____ also.

Find the word with *cy*. Write it. _____

Soft *c* Rule: When c is followed by ___, ___ or ___, it makes the sound of _____.

Write the Outlaw Words. _____   _____

Which letters are different in these two words? _____ Circle these letters.

Write the Classroom Words in capital letters on the lines below.

_____

_____

_____

Alternative Homework: In your reading book, find 12 words (at least 6 with *c*) that you want to learn. Write them in the Corrections column on page 31. Then write all of your spelling words and their definitions in your personal dictionary.

Find the spelling word that fits the meaning; then write it in syllables in the boxes.

1. This names a place to work. =

2. An orchestra presents this. =

3. This is the same as sure. =

4. This cloth hangs at a window. =

5. This is fair and equal treatment. =

6. A teacher writes this on perfect papers. =

7. We do this when we make something. =

8. This describes something happening in the near past. =

9. This person is a member of a nation. =

10. This is using something again in another way. =

11. People exchange names with those they don't know. =

12. This describes a measurement that is exact. =

13. We have this when we achieve what we try to do. =

14. This describes something that is needed. =

15. We do this when we repeat from memory. =

16. This equals one hundred years. =

17. This is the custom in most libraries. =

18. This is another word for honest and true. =

19. We do special things in honor of a day or person. =

Write in alphabetical order any spelling words not yet used on this page.

1. _____ 2. _____ 3. _____

4. _____ 5. _____ 6. _____

How many Classroom Words do you recall?

Write them; then look back to check.

Alternative Homework: Contest! How many different endings can you add to your spelling words? On a separate sheet of paper write the new words. You will earn one point for each correctly spelled word.

Mark the following statements *T* for true or *F* for false. Then underline the spelling word and write it in the box.

_____ 1. It is silly to celebrate your birthday.

_____ 2. Baseball players need to practice to do well in a concert.

_____ 3. Water is necessary for life.

_____ 4. A United States citizen is called an American.

_____ 5. There is always silence in my classroom.

_____ 6. Our 6–0 loss demonstrated our team's success.

_____ 7. Chickens produce eggs.

_____ 8. All curtains are made of lace.

_____ 9. Most Americans can recite the Pledge of Allegiance.

_____ 10. Bikes provide excellent transportation.

_____ 11. Most people live for a century.

_____ 12. The Declaration of Independence was signed recently.

_____ 13. All cats have tails, except bobcats.

_____ 14. You will often find a computer and telephone in an office.

_____ 15. A liar is a sincere person.

_____ 16. If you are sloppy, you will be precise in your work.

Write four true or false statements using spelling words not used above.

_____

_____

_____

_____

Write the Classroom Words on the steps beginning with the smallest.

Alternative Homework: Write ten true or false statements using your spelling words. Trade papers with a classmate and follow the directions above.

Answer the questions below by echoing words in the question.
Use spelling words in your answers whenever possible.

1. **Which holiday do you like to celebrate the most? Why?**
   I like to _____

   _____.

2. **What must you do to produce good school work?** *To* _____ *good school work you*

   must _____.

3. **Which country are you a citizen of?**
   I am a _____.

4. **Why is justice important for all people?** _____`

   _____.

5. **What concert would you like to attend?**
   I would like _____.

6. **Was your last school year a success? Why or why not?** *My last year was a* _____

   _____.

7. **How can you be certain an answer is correct?** *You can be* _____

   _____.

8. **Why is everyone working except the teacher?** *Everyone is* _____

   _____.

9. **Why is it necessary to tell the truth?** *It is* _____

   _____.

10. **What do you recycle?** *I* _____.

11. **Who would you like to be introduced to? Why?** *I would like* _____

    _____.

Write five questions using all of your Classroom Words.

_____

_____

_____

_____

_____

Alternative Homework: Write questions using eight of your spelling words; then trade papers with a
classmate and write answers to each other's questions.

Copy the words your teacher gives you under Classroom Words. Fold this page back along the dotted line so that only the Pretest column shows. Write the words your teacher dictates.

Pretest	Corrections	Spell*well* Words
1. _____	_____	1. admired
2. _____	_____	2. amazement
3. _____	_____	3. competing
4. _____	_____	4. described
5. _____	_____	5. entirely
6. _____	_____	6. frozen
7. _____	_____	7. improving
8. _____	_____	8. inhaling
9. _____	_____	9. lively
10. _____	_____	10. politeness
11. _____	_____	11. recognized
12. _____	_____	12. refused
13. _____	_____	13. required
14. _____	_____	14. revising
15. _____	_____	15. scraping
16. _____	_____	16. shaky
17. _____	_____	17. slavery
18. _____	_____	18. useful

Outlaw Words

19. _____	_____	19. Tuesday
20. _____	_____	20. Wednesday

Classroom Words

21. _____	_____	21. _____
22. _____	_____	22. _____
23. _____	_____	23. _____
24. _____	_____	24. _____
25. _____	_____	25. _____

Compare your words with the spelling list. Write the words you did not know in the Corrections column. If all, or all but one, of the words are correct, use the following for your spelling words: **description, examination, gratitude, immunizing, loveliness, recital, recognition,** and **scarecrow.** Write them in the Corrections column along with the Classroom Words; then do the Alternative Homework this week.

Look at the words below. Find spelling words that contain these small words, and write them beneath the appropriate word. (One column has two Spell*well* Words.) Next, think of other words that come from these words, and add them to each list. You may add prefixes and suffixes, and you may drop the last *e*.

tire   **prove**   **use**

_____   _____   _____

_____   _____   _____

_____   _____   _____

scribe   **mire**   **live**

_____   _____   _____

_____   _____   _____

_____   _____   _____

rap   **slave**   **pet**

_____   _____   _____

_____   _____   _____

Circle all the *ing* endings in your spelling words on page 36.

What happened to the final *e* of the root word? _____

Box all the *ed* and *en* endings in your spelling words.

What happened to the final *e* of the root word? _____

Underline the endings *ful*, *ment*, *ness*, *ry*, and *ly* on page 36.

What happened to the silent *e* this time? _____

Silent *e* Rule: When you add an ending that begins with a vowel,
you _____ the silent *e*.
When you add an ending beginning with a consonant,
you _____ the silent *e*.

Is the ending *y*, a vowel or a consonant? _____

What sound does it make? _____

Do you keep the *e* or drop it when adding *y* to a silent *e* word? _____

Add *y* to the root words below.

scare   **shake**   **slime**

_____   _____   _____

Alternative Homework: In your reading book, find 12 words that you want to learn. Write them in the Corrections column on page 36. Then write all of your spelling words and their definitions in your personal dictionary.

Find the word in each line that is improperly used or spelled and cross it out. Then choose a spelling word that better fits the sentence; write it on the line.

1. Her skill in figure skating was greatly mired. _____

2. Our team is completing with our arch rival today. _____

3. The pup was so likely that he knocked over the new lamp. _____

4. They are scrapping the plates before they wash them. _____

5. Every adult citizen is inquired to register before voting. _____

6. By January the lake had freezer over. _____

7. A jack can be very usually if you have a flat tire. _____

8. The author is devising some parts of the Spell*well* books. _____

9. She stared at the strange goblin in boredom. _____

10. He reorganized his aunt whom he hadn't seen in six years. _____

11. It is externally your fault if you are late for school. _____

12. We go on our field trip this Weddingday. _____

13. His hand was shaken as he tried to lift the weight. _____

14. Liberation was done away with in the South after the Civil War. _____

15. By exhaling deeply, you can take in a lot of oxygen. _____

16. The third day of the week is Toosday. _____

17. His politics toward the teacher won him respect. _____

18. Our class is reproving our spelling skills every week. _____

19. She inscribed the suspect to us in detail. _____

20. My parents fused to let us stay up late. _____

Sort your Classroom Words by writing them in the correct column below.

Nouns	Verbs	All Other Words
_____	_____	_____
_____	_____	_____
_____	_____	_____
_____	_____	_____
_____	_____	

Circle the Outlaw Words on page 36; then write the last five letters of these words. _____

Alternative Homework: Write a story about a doctor working in the jungle. Use at least five spelling words in your story. When you finish be sure to proofread what you have written.

Determine how the first two words go together, and then apply the same relationship to the last two words. Remember the words may be synonyms or antonyms; they may express whole to part relationships; they may describe a thing; or they may tell how it is used or done. The answers are all spelling words.

1. despised is to hated as appreciated is to _____

2. luxury is to necessity as optional is to _____

3. partially is to partly as completely is to _____

4. forgotten is to remembered as unknown is to _____

5. sure is to certain as unsteady is to _____

6. frightened is to fear as astonished is to _____

7. harmful is to helpful as useless is to _____

8. liquid is to solid as thawed is to _____

9. slow is to quick as dull is to _____

10. food is to eating as air is to _____

11. hostility is to friendliness as rudeness is to _____

12. peace is to war as freedom is to _____

13. yes is to no as accepted is to _____

14. repairing is to mending as changing is to _____

15. shoveling is to driveway as _____ is to windshield

16. failing is to worse as _____ is to better

17. lecture is to listening as contest is to _____

On the Face of It

Write your Outlaw and Classroom Words.
Circle the syllables in each word and count them;
then write the number of syllables on the line.

_____

_____

_____

_____

_____

_____

_____

Alternative Homework: Scramble the letters of eight of your spelling words. Then trade papers with another classmate with Alternative Homework this week, and unscramble each other's words.

Write eight complete sentences, choosing from the phrases below.
You may prefer to make your own phrases,
but be sure to include a spelling word in each.

enirely confused   scraping my knee   stared in amazement
revising the story   required reading   inhaling the smoke
the frozen icicles   described the accident   without any politeness
                                recognized the skateboard

_____

_____

_____

_____

_____

_____

_____

_____

_____

_____

_____

_____

_____

_____

_____

_____

_____

_____

_____

Write your Outlaw and Classroom Words, adding *s* or another ending if you can.

_____

_____

_____

Alternative Homework: Write eight phrases, using a spelling word in each one. Then write sentences
that include these phrases on the lines above.

Copy the words your teacher gives you under Classroom Words. Fold this page back along the dotted line so that only the Pretest column shows. Write the words your teacher dictates.

Spell*well* Words	Corrections	Pretest
1. alley		1.
2. beaver		2.
3. breathe		3.
4. disease		4.
5. donkey		5.
6. dreary		6.
7. ideal		7.
8. jockey		8.
9. kidney		9.
10. peaceful		10.
11. pleasing		11.
12. preach		12.
13. really		13.
14. reappear		14.
15. repeat		15.
16. season		16.
17. streamlined		17.
18. underneath		18.

Outlaw Words

19. area		19.
20. parallel		20.

Classroom Words

21.		21.
22.		22.
23.		23.
24.		24.
25.		25.

Compare your words with the spelling list. Write the words you did not know in the Corrections column. If all, or all but one, of the words are correct, use the following for your spelling words: **attorney, featured, greasiest, nausea, parallelogram, peacefulness, recreation,** and **upheaval.** Write them in the Corrections column along with the Classroom Words; then do the Alternative Homework this week.

Can you solve these equations to find a spelling word? When subtracting, cross out the letters; when adding, put the letters at the *end* of the word.

For example: worthless - th + d - less =

wor~~th~~less + d - less =
worlessd - less =
wor~~less~~d = word

1. parents - nts + a - p = _____

2. provide - v + al - pro = _____

3. nausea - u + son - na = _____

4. calculate - cu + y - at - c = _____

5. repaired - ed + eat - air = _____

6. brevity + a - v + the - ity = _____

7. quaking - ng + d - qua + ney = _____

8. abandon - a + key - ban = _____

9. separate - ate + all - se + el = _____

10. applesauce - ap + as - sauce + ing = _____

11. unprepared - ed + a - un + ch - par = _____

12. unreachable - un + ll - chable + y = _____

13. predispose - pose + ease - pre = _____

14. blundering + ne - ing + ath - bl = _____

15. displeased - sed + ce - l + ful - dis = _____

16. quadruple - up + ar - qua + y - l = _____

Which Spell*well* Words were not used? _____

_____

Make up questions using your Classroom Words; then write them along with the answers on the lines below.

_____

_____

_____

_____

_____

_____

_____

Alternative Homework: In your reading book, find 12 words (some with *ea* or *ey*) that you want to learn. Write them in the Corrections column on page 41. Then write all of your spelling words and their definitions in your personal dictionary.

Complete the puzzle below. Most of the words are spelling words.

ACROSS

1. Moving along on a frozen pond
4. Dull and gloomy
6. Considered perfect
8. Calm and quiet; not fighting
10. To appear again
12. Opposite of *happily*
14. A narrow street between buildings
15. To say or do again
17. To give a sermon
20. Designed to move quickly through air or water
23. What eyes do
24. An animal that builds dams
25. What fall from trees in autumn
27. A dry seed with a hard shell
29. Giving pleasure; agreeable
30. Horse-like animal with long ears
31. In a lower position; below

DOWN

2. An organ in the body
3. Person paid to ride a horse in a race
5. Truly; for real
7. What you lose when you stand up
8. Same distance apart at all points
9. What returning airplanes do
11. Frizzy; twisted in ringlets
13. A particular space, section, or region
16. What we breathe
18. Opposite of *opening*
19. To take air in and force it out
20. One of the four parts of the year
21. Opposite of *female*
22. Sickness
24. A group of musicians playing together
26. A sweet, crunchy fruit
28. What unlocks a door

Alternative Homework: Write as many of your spelling words as you can, connecting them horizontally or vertically as in a crossword puzzle. You may add other words if you need to.

How are the following words related?
In each case, think about how the first two words are connected.
Then apply the same relationship to find the missing spelling word.

1. **noisy** is to **loud** as **calm** is to _____

2. **lie** is to **falsely** as **fact** is to _____

3. **poverty** is to **starvation** as **bacteria** is to _____

4. **imperfect** is to **faulty** as **perfect** is to _____

5. **avenue** is to **wide** as _____ is to **narrow**

6. **sunny** is to **cloudy** as **cheerful** is to _____

7. **curved** is to **circle** as _____ is to **rectangle**

8. **complicated** is to **simple** as **fancy** is to _____

9. **attic** is to **overhead** as **basement** is to _____

10. **mild** is to **harsh** as _____ is to **distasteful**

11. **hare** is to **rabbit** as **mule** is to _____

12. **lecture** is to **speak** as **sermon** is to _____

13. **engineer** is to **train** as _____ is to **horse**

14. **nibbling** is to **mouse** as **gnawing** is to _____

15. **Wednesday** is to **weekday** as **winter** is to _____

16. **paint** is to **repaint** as **speak** is to _____

17. **sensory organ** is to **ear** as **body organ** is to _____

Write your Outlaw and Classroom Words in alphabetical order below.

_____

_____

_____

_____

_____

Write all the spelling words that begin with a vowel.

_____

_____

Alternative Homework: Use as many of your spelling words as you can in a paragraph about some kind of recreation that you enjoy. Tell what it is, where and when you do it, how it is done, and why you enjoy doing it. Be sure to include a description of any equipment you need for it.

Make as many new words as you can using these roots.
You may add letters at both the beginning and end
of each word. Include as many spelling words as you can.

ease

_____
_____
_____

key

_____
_____
_____

each

_____
_____
_____

eat

_____
_____
_____

ear

_____
_____
_____

all

_____
_____
_____

sea

_____
_____
_____

ream

_____
_____
_____

real

_____
_____
_____

Now write a short story using some of these new words.

_____
_____
_____
_____
_____
_____
_____
_____
_____
_____

Write your Classroom Words in color below.

_____
_____
_____
_____

Alternative Homework: Do the activity above.

Copy the words your teacher gives you under Classroom Words. Fold this page back along the dotted line so that only the Pretest column shows. Write the words your teacher dictates.

Pretest	**Corrections**	**Spell*well* Words**
1. _____	_____	1. achieve
2. _____	_____	2. agreement
3. _____	_____	3. cheese
4. _____	_____	4. degree
5. _____	_____	5. fierce
6. _____	_____	6. freeze
7. _____	_____	7. grief
8. _____	_____	8. handkerchief
9. _____	_____	9. infield
10. _____	_____	10. mischief
11. _____	_____	11. niece
12. _____	_____	12. piece
13. _____	_____	13. shield
14. _____	_____	14. sleeveless
15. _____	_____	15. squeeze
16. _____	_____	16. succeed
17. _____	_____	17. yield

Outlaw Words

18. _____	_____	18. interview
19. _____	_____	19. review
20. _____	_____	20. view

Classroom Words

21. _____	_____	21. _____
22. _____	_____	22. _____
23. _____	_____	23. _____
24. _____	_____	24. _____
25. _____	_____	25. _____

Compare your words with the spelling list. Write the words you did not know in the Corrections column. If all, or all but one, of the words are correct, use the following for your spelling words: **eerie, engineer, proceed, protein, puppeteer, receipt, refugee,** and **screeched.** Write them in the Corrections column along with the Classroom Words; then do the Alternative Homework this week.

Write the name of a cartoon character. _____

Now write each Spell*well* Word. Count the number of letters in common with the letters in this name. Give yourself 1 point for each letter in common. If there are *no* letters in common, give yourself 20 points. If there are more than five letters the same, give yourself 10 points.

For example, if you wrote "Garfield," it has three letters the same as the word *achieve* (*a, i, e*), but *squeeze* has only one letter in common.

Spell*well* Words	Points		Spell*well* Words	Points
1. _____	_____		10. _____	_____
2. _____	_____		11. _____	_____
3. _____	_____		12. _____	_____
4. _____	_____		13. _____	_____
5. _____	_____		14. _____	_____
6. _____	_____		15. _____	_____
7. _____	_____		16. _____	_____
8. _____	_____		17. _____	_____
9. _____	_____			

My Total Score: _____

Write your Outlaw and Classroom Words in syllables on the lines below; then write the number of syllables in each.

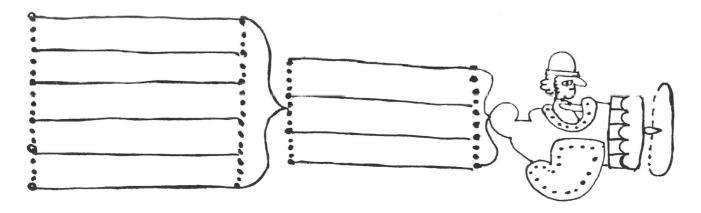

Alternative Homework: In your reading book, find 12 words that you would like to learn. Write them in the Corrections column on page 46. Then write all of your spelling words and their definitions in your personal dictionary.

Find the spelling word that fits the meaning; then write it in syllables in the boxes.

1. Mice like this very much. =

2. This is the same as sorrow. =

3. This is a close relative. =

4. We use this for the nose. =

5. This happens when everyone supports one idea. =

6. This is the area inside a baseball diamond. =

7. We do this to water to make ice cubes. =

8. This describes a lion or tiger. =

9. Usually this is part of applying for a job. =

10. This means "to give way." =

11. This shirt has no covering for the arms. =

12. This unit is the measurement on a thermometer. =

13. This means to accomplish or do something. =

14. To make juice, we do this to an orange. =

15. This names a section or part of the whole. =

16. This is to do something very well. =

17. This is important to do before a test. =

18. A knight might carry this in battle. =

19. A rascal is known for making this. =

20. From the top of a mountain, you have this. =

Write your Classroom Words on the steps below using a colored pen or pencil for the vowels.

Alternative Homework: On a separate sheet of paper, write twelve of your spelling words, one on each line. Next to each word, write a word related to it in some way; for example, it has the same root, is a plural, or adds an ending.

Sort the phrases below into the categories of noun phrase (words that name a person, place, or thing) and verb phrase (words that show action).

freeze your toes
a fierce bear
my youngest niece
review spelling words
a trade agreement
squeeze oranges

yield at the sign
a piece of cake
a view of the ocean
shield a child from harm
play the infield

eating pizza with cheese
succeed in school
a sleeveless shirt
a dirty handkerchief
a brief interview
ten degrees below zero

Noun Phrase

1. _____
2. _____
3. _____
4. _____
5. _____
6. _____
7. _____
8. _____
9. _____

Verb Phrase

1. _____
2. _____
3. _____
4. _____
5. _____
6. _____
7. _____
8. _____
9. _____

Fill in the last remaining blank with an appropriate phrase of your own.

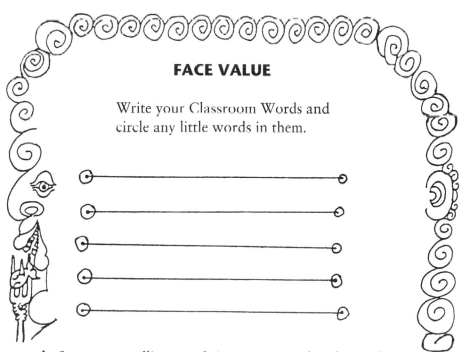

FACE VALUE

Write your Classroom Words and circle any little words in them.

Alternative Homework: Sort your spelling words into nouns and verbs, and write them in the columns above. Write any adjectives (words that describe) in the margins.

Look at the words below and think of words that rhyme. For example, under *bees* you might write *seas* or *keys*. Remember that rhyming words are not always spelled the same. Write at least two rhyming words. Next, write any spelling words that rhyme, dropping any endings. Then, looking at the words you have listed, write a poem of at least eight lines. After you read your poem aloud, give it a title.

bees

_____

_____

_____

_____

_____

_____

peeled

_____

_____

_____

_____

_____

_____

heave

_____

_____

_____

_____

_____

_____

crease

_____

_____

_____

_____

_____

reef

_____

_____

_____

_____

_____

_____

new

_____

_____

_____

_____

_____

_____

_____

_____

_____

_____

_____

_____

_____

_____

Alternative Homework: Do the exercise above or make rhymes from your own alternative spelling words; then write a poem using these words.

Copy the words your teacher gives you under Classroom Words. Fold this page back along the dotted line so that only the Pretest column shows. Write the words your teacher dictates.

Spell*well* Words	**Corrections**	**Pretest**
1. casual	_____	1. _____
2. continual	_____	2. _____
3. criminal	_____	3. _____
4. cripple	_____	4. _____
5. festival	_____	5. _____
6. knuckle	_____	6. _____
7. mammal	_____	7. _____
8. medical	_____	8. _____
9. mental	_____	9. _____
10. musical	_____	10. _____
11. rectangle	_____	11. _____
12. scramble	_____	12. _____
13. shuttle	_____	13. _____
14. tropical	_____	14. _____
15. untangle	_____	15. _____
16. unusual	_____	16. _____
17. vehicle	_____	17. _____

Outlaw Words

18. chemical	_____	18. _____
19. echo	_____	19. _____
20. orchestra	_____	20. _____

Classroom Words

21. _____	_____	21. _____
22. _____	_____	22. _____
23. _____	_____	23. _____
24. _____	_____	24. _____
25. _____	_____	25. _____

Compare your words with the spelling list. Write the words you did not know in the Corrections column. If all, or all but one, of the words are correct, use the following for your spelling words: **chemistry, controversial, echoes, hurdles, punctual, rectangular, tangible,** and **theatrical.** Write them in the Corrections column with the Classroom Words; then do the Alternative Homework this week.

Sort the Spell*well* Words according to the patterns below. Then add any Outlaw Words that follow these patterns.

Words with –*al*   **Words with –*le***

_____

_____

_____

_____

_____

_____   _____

_____   _____

_____   _____

_____   _____

_____   _____

_____   _____

Often a word ending in *al* is an adjective.
Write four Spell*well* Words ending in *al* that are adjectives or words that describe.

_____   _____

_____   _____

A word ending in *le* is often a noun.
Write four Spell*well* Words ending in *le* that are nouns or words that name something.

_____   _____

_____   _____

Look at the Outlaw Words. What sound does *ch* have in these words? _____
Write these words, beginning with the longest.

_____   _____   _____

Write your Classroom Words from longest to shortest.

_____

_____

_____

_____

_____

Alternative Homework: In your reading book, find 12 words (including some with -*al* or -*le*) that you want to learn. Write them in the Corrections column on page 51. Then write all of your spelling words and their definitions in your personal dictionary.

Look at each group below. Which spelling word will complete the puzzle? The horizontal word (across) is a synonym for, or means the same as, the spelling word. The vertical word (up and down) is its antonym or opposite. Write the spelling word in the squares.

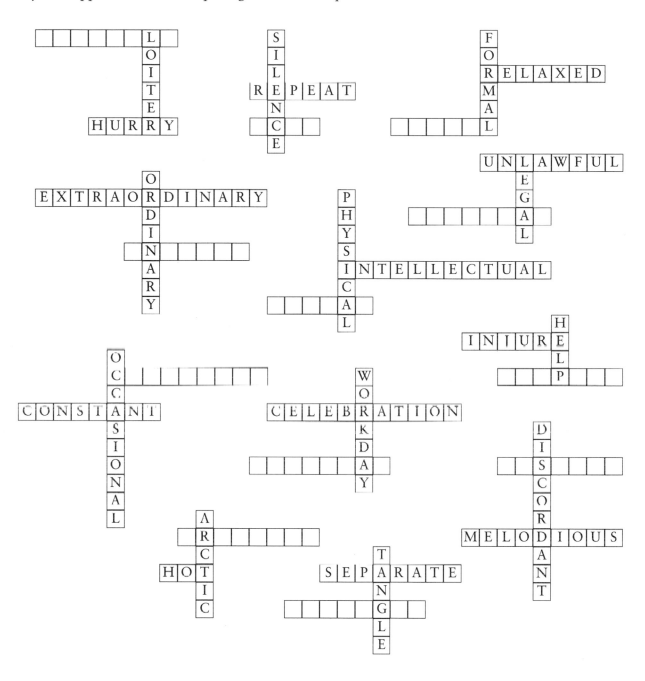

Write the spelling words that were *not* used on this page. There are thirteen of them.

_____

_____

_____

_____

Alternative Homework: Write your spelling words on a separate sheet of paper. Then write an antonym or a synonym next to as many words as you can.

The words in **boldface** are spelled in reverse order. Write the letters in correct order above those in boldface. Then read the story and answer the questions.

Do you know what is the most **suoregnad** bird in the world? Neither the eagle nor the ostrich compares with the large, shy **yrawossac**. This huge creature stands five feet tall and weighs 120 pounds. Because its wings are only long, bristle-like spines, it is impossible for this **lausunu** bird to fly. Although its body is covered with brownish-black feathers, the skin on its bare head and neck is brightly colored in red, blue, purple, and yellow. A bony **temleh** covers its head and is used for butting the heavy undergrowth as the cassowary **selbmarcs** through the thick rainforests of Australia, where it lives. The cassowary's long legs enable it to leap six feet in the air or to sprint along at a speed of thirty miles per hour, nearly as fast as a four-wheeled **elcihev**. Each foot of the cassowary has three toes with one ending in a long, sharp claw. This becomes a deadly **nopaew** in a fight. Although this bird is shy, watch out! A kick of its knife-sharp claw could easily **elppirc** or kill a person.

Do you remember the facts?

1. What is the most dangerous bird in the world? _____

_____

2. How much does it weigh? _____

3. What is unusual about this bird? _____

_____

_____

4. Why is the cassowary rarely seen? _____

5. How high can it jump? _____

6. Why is this shy bird so dangerous? _____

_____

_____

Write the Spell*well* Words with six letters.

_____   _____

_____

Write your Classroom Words anywhere on this page.

Alternative Homework: Choose an unusual bird, fish, or animal, and do research on it. Write a paragraph telling some of the things you learned. If possible, include some of your spelling words.

Can you dress up these simple sentences by adding the details asked for?

1. **Chemicals can be dangerous.**

   (*Tell what kind of chemicals.*) _____ can be dangerous.

   (*Tell why.*) _____

   _____ .

2. **The criminal jumps on a shuttle.**

   (*Tell where and when.*) _____

   _____ .

3. **Tropical vines are difficult to untangle.**

   (*Tell where.*) _____ .

   (*Now tell why.*) _____ .

4. **My knuckle is sore.**

   (*Tell which knuckle.*) _____ .

   (*Now tell why it is sore.*) _____ .

5. **They need continual medical treatment.**

   (*Tell who.*) _____ need _____

   (*Now tell why.*) _____

   _____ .

6. **The festival is my favorite.**

   (*Tell which festival.*) _____ .

   (*Tell when it is and why you like it.*) _____

   _____ .

7. **We heard a musical echo.**

   (*Tell what it was and where.*) _____

   _____ .

8. **The room was a rectangle.**

   (*Tell what kind of room and its size.*) _____

   (*Tell the best thing about it.*) _____

   _____ .

9. **The orchestra plays.**

   (*Tell which orchestra.*) _____ .

   (*Tell what it plays.*) _____ .

   (*Add when and how it plays.*) _____

   _____ .

Alternative Homework: Circle your first nine spelling words. Now write detailed sentences using each of these words. Be sure to include some of the following information: what, when, where, how, and why.

Copy the words your teacher gives you under Classroom Words. Fold this page back along the dotted line so that only the Pretest column shows. Write the words your teacher dictates.

Pretest	**Corrections**	**Spell*well* Words**
1. _____	_____	1. angel
2. _____	_____	2. arrange
3. _____	_____	3. average
4. _____	_____	4. cabbage
5. _____	_____	5. challenge
6. _____	_____	6. dodge
7. _____	_____	7. general
8. _____	_____	8. gigantic
9. _____	_____	9. margin
10. _____	_____	10. messenger
11. _____	_____	11. original
12. _____	_____	12. pledge
13. _____	_____	13. shortage
14. _____	_____	14. suggest
15. _____	_____	15. surgery
16. _____	_____	16. trudge
17. _____	_____	17. village
18. _____	_____	18. voyage

Outlaw Words

19. _____	_____	19. fragile
20. _____	_____	20. garage

Classroom Words

21. _____	_____	21. _____
22. _____	_____	22. _____
23. _____	_____	23. _____
24. _____	_____	24. _____
25. _____	_____	25. _____

Compare your words with the spelling list. Write the words you did not know in the Corrections column. If all, or all but one, of the words are correct, use the following for your spelling words: **foliage, gadget, geometry, gorgeous, language, manageable, privilege,** and **register**. Write them in the Corrections column along with the Classroom Words; then do the Alternative Homework this week.

Thirteen spelling words have been divided into syllables and then separated into two columns. Make the words whole again by drawing a line from the first syllable in column one to the remaining syllable or syllables in column two. Then write the whole word on the line next to the last syllable.

1. ar   gest   _____

2. mar   lage   _____

3. sug   sen • ger   _____

4. vil   bage   _____

5. frag   range   _____

6. cab   gin   _____

7. voy   lenge   _____

8. sur   ile   _____

9. chal   er • al   _____

10. gen   ger • y   _____

11. mes   rig • i • nal _____

12. o   gan • tic   _____

13. gi   age   _____

Circle the words on page 56 that end with *dge*.
What kind of vowel comes before *dge*? Long or short? _____

Write the rule: After a short vowel, use the letters _____ to spell the /j/ sound. After a long vowel, use *ge*.

Using the rule above, add *dge* or *ge* to the letters below to make common words.

fu _____   ple _____   ran _____

ca _____   do   _____   sta _____

ra _____   ju   _____   tru _____

Add *s* or some other ending to each of your Classroom Words. _____

_____

_____

Write the Outlaw Words spelling them aloud. Then circle the vowels.

_____

Alternative Homework: In your reading book, find 12 words that you want to learn. Some should have *g*. Write them in the Corrections column on page 56. Then write all of your spelling words and their definitions in your personal dictionary.

Complete the puzzle below. Most of the words are spelling words.

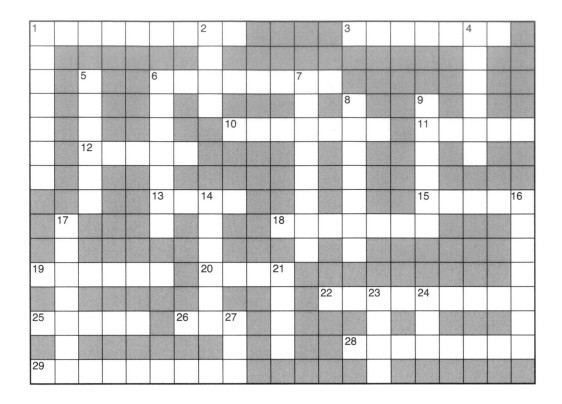

ACROSS

1. To confront boldly or dare
3. Not out of the ordinary
6. Not having enough; a lack
10. A medical operation
11. A musical instrument with pipes
12. To keep away from by moving aside
13. Opposite of *different*
15. Opposite of *coming*
18. A very small town
19. To walk slowly and with effort
20. Donate
22. One who delivers a message
25. One with wings who wears a halo
26. A small insect that lives in a hill
28. Fresh and new; inventive
29. A figure with four parallel sides

DOWN

1. A green or red vegetable with leaves
2. To get taller
4. A place to keep a car
5. To give an oath or promise
6. To offer an idea
7. Huge
8. Easily broken
9. A trip by water or through space
14. The white border around a page
16. The head officer of an army
17. To make plans or put in order
21. A sound that reverberates or bounces back
23. Certain
24. It comes from a chicken
27. A small peg where a golf ball is placed

Alternative Homework: Write as many of your spelling words as you can, connecting them horizontally or vertically as in a crossword puzzle. You may add other words if you need to.

Mark the following statements *T* for true or *F* for false. Then underline the spelling word and write it in the box.

_____ 1. An angel has wings.

_____ 2. There is a shortage of candy in the United States.

_____ 3. It is easy to get lost in a village.

_____ 4. Many kids like to play dodge ball.

_____ 5. A monkey is gigantic.

_____ 6. Rubber tires are fragile.

_____ 7. Cabbage is everyone's favorite vegetable.

_____ 8. You can keep a car in a garage.

_____ 9. It is best to be an average student.

_____ 10. In general, cats are bigger than dogs.

_____ 11. You can run home after having surgery.

_____ 12. A challenge can be fun.

_____ 13. Most books have margins.

_____ 14. It is easy to arrange a visit with President Roosevelt.

Write three true or false statements using spelling words that were not used above.

_____

_____

Write true or false statements using all of your Classroom Words.

_____

_____

_____

_____

_____

Alternative Homework: Write true or false statements like those above, using eight of your spelling words. Write them on the lines above.

Answer the questions below by echoing words in the question. Use spelling words in your answers if you can.

1. When should you dodge a ball instead of catching it? _____

_____

2. What is a challenge for you?   _____

_____

3. What do you own that is fragile?   _____

_____

4. What is an average test score? _____

5. What voyage would you like to take?_____

_____

6. When is it fun to clean a garage?_____

_____

7. Why don't gigantic animals make good pets?   _____

_____

8. Where might a general and his troops trudge?   _____

_____

9. What change in class would you suggest to the teacher? _____

_____

10. How do you pledge the flag?   _____

_____

11. What can you do to avoid a shortage of water?   _____

_____

Write in alphabetical order the spelling words not used on this page (including your Classroom Words).

_____

_____

_____

_____

Alternative Homework: Using your first eight spelling words, write questions like those above. Trade papers with another student, and answer each other's questions by echoing the words in the question.

Copy the words your teacher gives you under Classroom Words. Fold this page back along the dotted line so that only the Pretest column shows. Write the words your teacher dictates.

Spell*well* Words	**Corrections**	**Pretest**
1. acceptance	_____	1. _____
2. advance	_____	2. _____
3. allowance	_____	3. _____
4. attendance	_____	4. _____
5. conference	_____	5. _____
6. confidence	_____	6. _____
7. difference	_____	7. _____
8. disappearance	_____	8. _____
9. distance	_____	9. _____
10. evidence	_____	10. _____
11. experience	_____	11. _____
12. finance	_____	12. _____
13. importance	_____	13. _____
14. independence	_____	14. _____
15. reference	_____	15. _____
16. sequence	_____	16. _____
17. violence	_____	17. _____

Outlaw Words

18. conscience	_____	18. _____
19. science	_____	19. _____
20. scientist	_____	20. _____

Classroom Words

21. _____	_____	21. _____
22. _____	_____	22. _____
23. _____	_____	23. _____
24. _____	_____	24. _____
25. _____	_____	25. _____

Compare your words with the spelling list. Write the words you did not know in the Corrections column. If all, or all but one, of the words are correct, use the following for your spelling words: **brilliance, commencement, scientific, inconvenience, maintenance, preference, financial,** and **significance.** Write them in the Corrections column with the Classroom Words; then do the Alternative Homework this week.

Sort the *Spellwell* Words according to the patterns below. Then add any Outlaw Words that follow these patterns.

Words Ending with *ance*   **Words Ending with *ence***

_____   _____

_____   _____

_____   _____

_____   _____

_____   _____

_____   _____

_____   _____

_____   _____

_____   _____

FACE UP TO IT!

Write the three Outlaw Words: _____

_____

In the first Outlaw Word,
sci sounds like _____ .

In the other Outlaw Words,
sci sounds like _____ .

Write your Classroom Words around the
outside of the head, beginning with the
shortest and ending
with the longest.

Alternative Homework: In your reading book, find 12 words (including some with *-ance* or *-ence)* that you want to learn. Write them in the Corrections column on page 61. Then write all of your spelling words and their definitions in your personal dictionary.

Look at each group below. Which spelling word will complete the puzzle? The horizontal word (across) is a synonym for, or means the same as, the spelling word. The vertical word (up and down) is its antonym or opposite. Write the spelling word in the squares.

```
        S                                      I
 V A R I A T I O N                            G
        M                        K N O W L E D G E
        E                                      O
        N             S                        R
        E             L                        A
        S             A                        N
                      V                        C
                      E                        E
           F R E E D O M
                      R
                      Y

 R                                                G
 E                                                E
 T                       N                        N
 P R O G R E S S    R E M O T E N E S S          T
 R                       A                        L
 E                       R              R A G E   E
 A                       N                        N
 T                       E                        E
                         S             U          S
                         S             N          S
                                       I
 S                                     M
 H                                     P
 Y                       S        [across]
 N                       U
 E                       P
 S                       E
 A S S U R A N C E       R    S I G N I F I C A N C E
                         S              C
                         T              E
 A          I N V E S T I G A T I O N
 B                       T                   R
 P R E S E N C E         I                   E
 N                       O                   J
 C                       N                   E
 E                                 A D M I T T A N C E
                           E                 I
                           M                 O
                           E                 N
                           R
                           G
                           E
                 V A N I S H M E N T
                           C
                           E
```

Write the Spell*well* and Outlaw Words that were not used on this page. _____

_____

_____

_____

Alternative Homework: Write any twelve spelling words. Write an antonym next to those that have one. If there is none, write an equal sign (=) and a synonym next to the word.

Decipher the following message, using the letters that correspond to the numbers below. Write the letters over the numbers as shown. Circle the spelling words you find in the message, and write them on the lines below.

A	B	C	D	E	F	G	H	I	J	K	L	M	N	O	P	Q	R	S	T	U	V	W	X	Y	Z
1	2	3	4	5	6	7	8	9	10	11	12	13	14	15	16	17	18	19	20	21	22	23	24	25	26

C H I E F

`3 8 9 5 6` : `1 13` `1 20` `23 15 18 12 4`

`3 15 14 6 5 18 5 14 3 5` `15 14` `1 4 22 1 14 3 5 4`

`19 3 9 5 14 3 5` `15 6` `7 18 1 22 5` `9 13 16 15 18 20 1 14 3 5`

`20 15` `5 1 18 20 8` . `13 1 14 25` `19 3 9 5 14 20 9 19 20 19`

`23 9 20 8 15 21 20` `3 15 14 19 3 9 5 14 3 5` `9 14`

`1 20 20 5 14 4 1 14 3 5` . `14 5 5 4` `8 5 12 16` `23 9 20 8`

`4 9 19 1 16 16 5 1 18 1 14 3 5` `15 6` `19 5 3 18 5 20`

`6 9 12 5 19` . `8 1 22 5` `5 22 9 4 5 14 3 5` `20 8 1 20`

`19 15 13 5` `9 14` `1 21 4 9 5 14 3 5` `13 1 25` `21 19 5`

`22 9 15 12 5 14 3 5` . `19 5 14 4` `1 7 5 14 20 19` `23 9 20 8`

`5 24 16 5 18 9 5 14 3 5` . `1 7 5 14 20` `24 24 24`

_____

_____

_____

_____

Write the Classroom Words in capital letters anywhere on this page.

Alternative Homework: Do the activity above.

Write a newspaper story using one of the headlines below. Circle the headline you will use. Try to include all the necessary facts: *who, what, where, when, how,* and *why.* Use some spelling words in your story.

COACH LOSES CONFIDENCE AFTER DEFEAT
PET DOG MAKES A DIFFERENCE
VIOLENCE ON T.V. BAD FOR KIDS?
ANCIENT REFERENCE BOOK FOUND IN TOMB
LONG-DISTANCE RUNNER WINS FOR KENYA
WINNER GIVES ACCEPTANCE SPEECH
SEQUENCE OF STORMS LEAVES SEVERE DAMAGE
ALLOWANCE TEACHES KIDS FINANCE

_____

_____

_____

_____

_____

_____

_____

_____

_____

_____

_____

_____

_____

_____

_____

_____

_____

Write your Classroom Words below and circle any little words in them.

_____

_____

_____

Alternative Homework: Make a headline using one of your spelling words. Then write a news story, following the directions above.

Copy the words your teacher gives you under Classroom Words. Fold this page back along the dotted line so that only the Pretest column shows. Write the words your teacher dictates.

Pretest	Corrections	Spell*well* Words
1. _____	_____	1. addition
2. _____	_____	2. competition
3. _____	_____	3. condition
4. _____	_____	4. constitution
5. _____	_____	5. direction
6. _____	_____	6. election
7. _____	_____	7. elevation
8. _____	_____	8. imagination
9. _____	_____	9. imitation
10. _____	_____	10. information
11. _____	_____	11. observation
12. _____	_____	12. population
13. _____	_____	13. position
14. _____	_____	14. question
15. _____	_____	15. revolution
16. _____	_____	16. situation
17. _____	_____	17. transportation

Outlaw Words

18. _____	_____	18. enough
19. _____	_____	19. rough
20. _____	_____	20. tough

Classroom Words

21. _____	_____	21. _____
22. _____	_____	22. _____
23. _____	_____	23. _____
24. _____	_____	24. _____
25. _____	_____	25. _____

Compare your words with the spelling list. Write the words you did not know in the Corrections column. If all, or all but one, of the words are correct, use the following for your spelling words: **condensation, expedition, generation, nation, objection, preposition, qualification,** and **relaxation.** Write them in the Corrections column along with the Classroom Words; then do the Alternative Homework this week.

Can you solve these equations to find a spelling word? When subtracting, cross out the letters; when adding, put the letters at the end of the word.

For example: worthless - th + d - less =
worthless + d - less =
worlessd - less =
worlessd = word

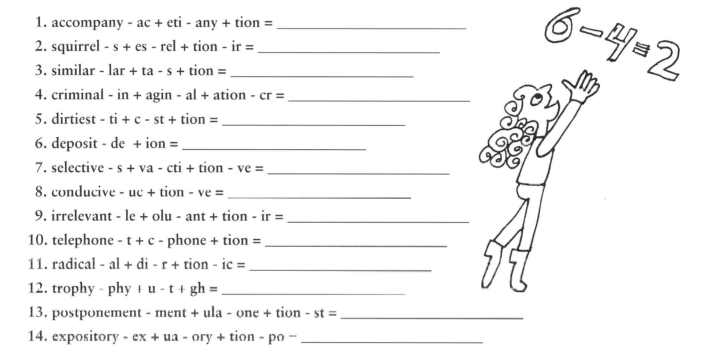

1. accompany - ac + eti - any + tion = _____

2. squirrel - s + es - rel + tion - ir = _____

3. similar - lar + ta - s + tion = _____

4. criminal - in + agin - al + ation - cr = _____

5. dirtiest - ti + c - st + tion = _____

6. deposit - de + ion = _____

7. selective - s + va - cti + tion - ve = _____

8. conducive - uc + tion - ve = _____

9. irrelevant - le + olu - ant + tion - ir = _____

10. telephone - t + c - phone + tion = _____

11. radical - al + di - r + tion - ic = _____

12. trophy - phy + u - t + gh = _____

13. postponement - ment + ula - one + tion - st = _____

14. expository - ex + ua - ory + tion - po - _____

Write your Classroom Words, sorting them into three categories: nouns (persons, places, things), verbs (actions a person can do), and all other words.

Nouns   **Verbs**   **All Other Words**

_____   _____   _____

_____   _____   _____

_____   _____   _____

_____   _____   _____

Which spelling words were not used on this page?

_____   _____

_____   _____

_____   _____

Alternative Homework: In your reading book, find 12 words that you want to learn. Write them in the Corrections column on page 66. Then write all of your spelling words and their definitions in your personal dictionary.

Find the word in each line that is improperly used or spelled and cross it out.
Then choose a spelling word that better fits the sentence; write it on the line.

1. An electric for United States president is held every four years. _____

2. In first grade we learned additional and subtraction. _____

3. The populate of the remote island was only ten people. _____

4. Eating one peanut is never enoch. _____

5. The American Revolt began in 1775. _____

6. Do you have the informative to write a story? _____

7. A counterfeit bill must be a good imitate to trick people. _____

8. Despite the accident, the car was still in good conditional. _____

9. People voted for changes in the state constituent. _____

10. The teacher asked if there were any quests. _____

11. There are two servation decks on top of the skyscraper. _____

12. After the storm, the sea was rouge and wavy. _____

13. When two teams try hard to win, there is completion. _____

14. Planes provide fast transpiration. _____

15. It is though to be the youngest in a family. _____

16. The elevator of Mt. Misery is 3000 feet. _____

17. Use your imagine, and pretend to be a bird. _____

18. When the car broke down, we were in a difficult situate. _____

Which Spell*well* Words tell the place where a thing is and the way it is moving or pointing?

_____   _____   _____

Write the Classroom Words, adding
an ending to each if you can.

_____

_____

_____

_____

_____

Alternative Homework: Write a story about your generation and some of the things you and your
friends enjoy doing. Try to use some prepositions in your story.

The words in **boldface** are spelled in reverse order. Write the letters in correct order above those in boldface. Then read the story and answer the questions.

Montserrat, once a rugged, scenic, but thriving island in the West Indies, has met with disaster. This small island with an **noitavele** of 3002 feet occupies a **noitisop** half-way down the Leeward Island chain. Its dormant **onaclov** had smoldered for many years, but in 1997 it began to erupt, sending hot sand, gases, and rocks in the **noltcerid** of the capital, Plymouth. The town was gradually destroyed. With each new eruption the **noitautis** grew worse. When the airport and a huge church were both buried, most people decided they had had **hguone**. They left for nearby islands or for England, using whatever **noitatropsnart** they could find. Montserrat's **noltalupop**, once 14,000 people, is now only a few hundred. The present **snoitidnoc** on the island are terrible: no jobs, no crops, no grass for livestock! The latest **snoitavresbo** of the volcano show only minor eruptions. But the **noitseuq** remains—will people return to Montserrat to rebuild after large buildings in **noitidda** to entire towns have completely disappeared?

Do you remember the facts?

1. Where is Montserrat located? _____

2. What is the capital of Montserrat? _____

3. Describe the erupting material that buried the island. _____

_____

4. What was the population of the island before the volcano erupted in 1997? _____

5. Do you think people will return to Monserrat to rebuild? Explain your answer. _____

_____

_____

Write the Spell*well* Words with eleven or more letters. _____

_____

_____

Write your Outlaw and Classroom Words anywhere on this page.

Alternative Homework: On a separate sheet of paper, write twelve of your spelling words, one on each line. Next to each word, write a word related to it in some way; it may be the plural of the word or have the same root.

Make as many new words as you can using these roots. You may add letters at both the beginning and end of each word, and you may drop a final *e* to add an ending. Include as many spelling words as you can.

mit
_____
_____
_____
_____

lect
_____
_____
_____
_____

form
_____
_____
_____
_____

quest
_____
_____
_____
_____

port
_____
_____
_____

imagine
_____
_____
_____
_____

serve
_____
_____
_____
_____

direct
_____
_____
_____
_____

Write the Spell*well* Word that begins with *r*. _____

Write sentences using your Outlaw and Classroom Words.

_____
_____
_____
_____
_____
_____
_____
_____

Alternative Homework: Do the activity above.

Copy the words your teacher gives you under Classroom Words. Fold this page back along the dotted line so that only the Pretest column shows. Write the words your teacher dictates.

Spell*well* Words	**Corrections**	**Pretest**
1. athletic		1.
2. atmosphere		2.
3. biography		3.
4. fifth		4.
5. fiftieth		5.
6. hemisphere		6.
7. microphone		7.
8. paragraph		8.
9. phantom		9.
10. rather		10.
11. seventh		11.
12. symphony		12.
13. telegraph		13.
14. theater		14.
15. themselves		15.
16. thermometer		16.
17. triumph		17.

Outlaw Words

18. thorough		18.
19. though		19.
20. through		20.

Classroom Words

21.		21.
22.		22.
23.		23.
24.		24.
25.		25.

Compare your words with the spelling list. Write the words you did not know in the Corrections column. If all, or all but one, of the words are correct, use the following for your spelling words: **philosopher, autobiography, physician, stealthy, sympathy, thistle, triumphant,** and **threadbare**. Write them in the Corrections column along with the Classroom Words; then do the Alternative Homework this week.

Sixteen spelling words have been divided into syllables and then separated into two columns. Make the words whole again by drawing a line from the syllable or syllables in column one to the remaining syllables in column two. Write the whole word on the line next to the last syllable.

1. hem • i   pho • ny = _____

2. them   graph =   _____

3. at • mos   sphere = _____

4. sym   e • ter = _____

5. tri   selves = _____

6. ther • mom   ra • phy = _____

7. tel • e   graph = _____

8. par • a   phere = _____

9. phan   umph = _____

10. bi • og   enth = _____

11. mi • cro   ti • eth = _____

12. sev   tom = _____

13. fif   phone = _____

14. the   let • ic = _____

15. rath   a • ter = _____

16. ath   er = _____

Two letters that make *one* sound, such as *sh, ch, th, ph, wh,* are called digraphs. The letters *ph* have the sound of _____ .

Write the Outlaw Words. _____ _____ _____

Circle the letters that are the same in each word. Write them. _____

In two of these words, the letters _____ sound like /ō/.

In the other Outlaw Word, these same letters have the sound of /o͞o/.

Write questions using your Classroom Words.

_____

_____

_____

_____

_____

Alternative Homework: In your reading book, find 12 words that you want to learn. (At least five words should have digraphs.) Write them in the Corrections column on page 71. Then write all of your spelling words and their definitions in your personal dictionary.

Complete the puzzle below. Many of the words are spelling words.

ACROSS

2. A person who works in science
6. Animals with big front teeth for gnawing
8. Weep
9. A name for male cats
11. A group of sentences about one idea
13. Opposite of *she*
14. Even if; however
16. Having to do with the North or South Pole
18. Fragrant flowers that grow on a bush
20. Opposite of *bore*
21. Leaving nothing out; careful and complete
23. One half of the earth
25. The story of someone's life
28. A tool used to loosen soil and weeds
29. Comes after *fourth*
31. Way of sending a message over wires
32. Their own selves
33. Having to do with sports

DOWN

1. A sound that comes back to you
2. A large orchestra
3. Very cold and slippery
4. A drop of water that comes from the eye
5. An instrument used to measure temperature
6. Instead; more willingly
7. Not bright; having little light
10. The layer of gases around the earth
12. A ghost
14. Finished
15. What you speak into to be heard
17. A victory
19. Part of the armor a knight carried
22. Comes before *eighth*
24. A place to see movies or plays
26. The outer covering of a nut
27. Partner of *salt*
30. A thought or plan

Alternative Homework: Write as many of your spelling words as you can, connecting them horizontally or vertically as in a crossword puzzle. You may add other words if you need to.

Sort the phrases below into the categories of tangible things (able to be touched) and intangible things (not able to be touched).

a typewritten paragraph   fifth grade

a symphony orchestra   a mysterious phantom

the earth's atmosphere   theater tickets

a telegraph operator   outdoor thermometer

an athletic triumph   the northern hemisphere

fiftieth birthday   biography of Jackie Robinson

Tangible

1. _____
2. _____
3. _____
4. _____
5. _____
6. _____

Intangible

1. _____
2. _____
3. _____
4. _____
5. _____
6. _____

Sort your Classroom Words, using the same categories; then write them in the correct columns.

7. _____
8. _____
9. _____
10. _____
11. _____

7. _____
8. _____
9. _____
10. _____
11. _____

Now fill the remaining lines with appropriate phrases.

Write the Spell*well* Words that have *v* in them.

_____   _____

Write the correct Outlaw Words in the sentences below.

We walked quickly _____ the forest even _____

it was very dense and dark. Nevertheless, we were very _____

in our search for the missing backpack.

Alternative Homework: Sort your spelling words, using the categories and lines above.

Write a newspaper story using one of the headlines below. Circle the headline you will use. Try to include all the necessary facts: *who, what, where, when, how,* and *why.* Use some spelling words in your story.

ATHLETIC CONTEST SCHEDULED FRIDAY
FIFTIETH CALLER WINS JACKPOT
POLLUTION AFFECTING ATMOSPHERE
SECRET MICROPHONE REVEALS SURPRISE
FIFTH GRADER WINS SWEEPSTAKES
CARDINALS TRIUMPH AGAIN!
JETS WOULD RATHER NOT LOSE STAR PLAYER
WARMING TREND IN NORTHERN HEMISPHERE

_____
_____
_____
_____
_____
_____
_____
_____
_____
_____
_____
_____
_____

The root *graph* means "to write or imprint." What does *paragraph* mean? _____

_____

What is a book written about someone's life called? _____

The root *sphere* means "globe." *Hemi* means "half." What is a *hemisphere*? _____

_____

The root *phone* means "sound." Which two spelling words are based on this root?

_____   _____   _____

Write your Classroom Words on the lines below and color the vowels red.

_____
_____
_____
_____

Alternative Homework: Make a headline using one of your spelling words. Then, following the directions above, write a news story on the lines provided.

Word List for Spell*well* D

acceptance
achieve
addition
admired
advance
advertise
agreement
alley
allowance
amazement
angel
area
arrange
arrest
assorted
athletic
atmosphere
attachment
attendance
average
bananas
beaver
behavior
berry
biography
borrow
breathe
brotherhood
bury
cabbage
calendar
cartoon
casual
celebrate
century
certain
challenge
charming
cheese
chemical
childhood
chocolate
citizen
closet
competing
competition
concert
condition
conference
confidence
conscience
constitution
continual
credit
criminal
cripple
cucumber
curly
curtain
dampness
degree

delightful
demand
department
deposit
described
desert
diameter
difference
direction
disappearance
disease
distance
disturb
divide
dodge
donkey
dozen
drama
dreary
duplex
during
echo
election
elevation
enough
entirely
environment
equal
equator
equipment
errand
error
evidence
excellent
except
excitement
experience
export
familiar
favorite
federal
fellowship
festival
fierce
fifth
fiftieth
figures
finance
flavor
forbid
fragile
freeze
frequent
frozen
furnish
garage
general
gigantic
gorilla
governor
grammar

grief
guard
guitar
habitat
hamburger
handkerchief
harvest
hemisphere
history
humor
ideal
imagination
imitation
importance
improving
independence
infield
information
inhaling
inspector
interview
introduce
inventory
iron
jockey
jury
justice
kidney
knuckle
lively
lunar
mammal
marble
margin
medical
medium
melody
membership
mental
messenger
microwave
microphone
mirror
mischief
modern
murder
muscular
musical
narrowness
natural
necessary
niece
normal
novel
observation
occur
office
orbit
orchestra
ordinary
original

painful
paragraph
parallel
particular
pattern
peaceful
penmanship
phantom
piano
piece
pleasing
pledge
plural
polar
politeness
popular
population
position
preach
precise
president
pretend
prisoner
produce
products
propeller
quarrel
quarter
question
quiet
rather
really
reappear
recently
recite
recognized
recommend
rectangle
recycle
reference
reflect
refused
repeat
required
review
revising
revolution
rodent
rough
science
scientist
scramble
scraping
season
sequence
settlement
seventh
several
shaky
shield
shortage

shuttle
sickness
silence
similar
sincere
situation
slavery
sleeveless
slogan
sparkle
squeeze
squirrel
streamlined
succeed
success
suggest
support
surgery
surprised
sword
symphony
talented
telegraph
theater
themselves
thermometer
thirsty
thorough
though
through
total
tough
toward
transportation
travel
triangle
triumph
tropical
trudge
Tuesday
underneath
United States
untangle
unusual
useful
vapor
vehicle
verdict
view
village
violence
visitor
volume
voyage
Wednesday
wilderness
wonderful
yield